page 2

Alice   Jenny

Mike   Steve

page 7

6	2	8	8
1	4	2	5

page 15

8	6	5
8	0	1

page 25

CW00865646

page 10

(illustrations of animals arranged in a grid: donkey, cow, duck, hen, sheep, buffalo; hippo, zebra, butterfly, elephant, lion, rhino; giraffe, seal, whale, crocodile, frog, snake; donkey, cow, duck, hen, sheep, buffalo; hippo, zebra, butterfly, elephant, lion, rhino; giraffe, seal, whale, crocodile, frog, snake)

page 19

<	<
>	>
=	<
0.25	0.2
0.07	0.02
0.5	0.05

(three clocks)

page 17

(illustrations of vegetables: tomatoes, carrots, potatoes, radishes, cabbages)

page 31

page 18

Leap Ahead Workbook

8-9 years

Leap Ahead

Maths
Home learning made fun

Key Stage 2

igloobooks

Reading and comparing

Four friends are competing on the television game show *Friends of Fortune*. Their podiums show their winnings at the end of Round 1. Write each contestant's winnings in words. Steve's is done for you.

| Steve £1807 | Jenny £3050 | Mike £2246 | Alice £1355 |

One thousand, eight hundred and seven

3050   22146   1355

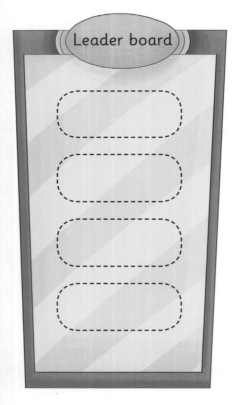

Now put the contestants in order on the leader board, using the four names on the sticker sheet. Put the person with the most money at the top and the person with the least money at the bottom.

At the end of Round 2, Alice has won £2000, Jenny has lost £500, Mike has lost £90 and Steve has won £800. Write everyone's new totals after Round 2.

Alice ....   Jenny ....

Mike ....   Steve ....

2

Answers on page 32

The scores below show how much money the players had won by the end of Round 3. In Round 4, players win or lose multiples of £100. Based on this, answer the questions below.

ROUND 3 SCORES

| Alice: £5435 | Jenny: £3930 | Mike: £5859 | Steve: £4518 |

(a) How much money does Alice need to win to take the lead?

....

(b) How much does Jenny need to win to catch up with Steve?

....

(c) How much does Mike need to win to pass his target of £6500?

....

The computer system has got a virus which is causing the contestants' winnings for Round 5 to be calculated incorrectly. Explain the mistake for each contestant, and write the correct answer below.

	Round 4 scores	Amount won or lost in Round 5	New score
Alice	£6560	Lost £500	£7060
Jenny	£3546	Won £300	£6546
Mike	£7355	Won £50	£7395
Steve	£4290	Won £800	£4090

Alice: ....

Jenny: ....

Mike: ....

Steve: ....

Answers on page 32

PARENT TIP: When your child walks up and down the stairs, encourage them to count in different multiples of 10 and 100 from different starting points. For example, start at 345 and count in 200s, or start at 840 and count backwards in multiples of 30.

3

Rounding

This table shows the visitor numbers for the first 6 months at a new trampoline park. Complete the table by rounding the numbers for each month to the nearest 10, 100 and 1000.

	Visitor numbers	Rounded to the nearest 10	Rounded to the nearest 100	Rounded to the nearest 1000
January	2345			
February	2767			
March	3698			
April	3064			
May	4002			
June	2986			

For July, August and September, the manager Sue has got the visitor numbers in a muddle because they all contain the same four digits: 2, 3, 6, 8. Can you work out what the visitor numbers were for each month, using Sue's rounded numbers?

	Visitor numbers	Rounded to nearest 10	Rounded to nearest 100	Rounded to nearest 1000
July		2860	2900	3000
August		2640	2600	3000
September		3270	3300	3000

Answers on page 32

(a) Sue works out the visitor numbers for the rest of the year. First, she rounds the visitor numbers for October to 2300 to the nearest hundred. What could the number of visitors have been? Give three possibilities.

....

(b) What are the highest and lowest possible visitor numbers?

Highest ....   Lowest ....

(c) She forgot to add a birthday party to October's numbers. Including the birthday party, October's number rounds to 2400 to the nearest hundred. What are the highest and lowest visitor numbers there could have been in October?

Highest ....   Lowest ....

(d) In November, the number of visitors was 3966. Round this number to the nearest 100 and nearest 1000. What do you notice?

....

....

(e) In December, there were 7203 visitors. Sue says that 7203 to the nearest 10 is 7200 but she is confused because this is a multiple of 100. Can you help her understand?

....

....

(f) Sue says that if she had had one more visitor in January, the number would have rounded to 9000 to the nearest 1000. How many visitors did she have?

....

Answers on page 32

5

Adding 4-digit numbers

These are the supporter numbers for two football teams at the first five football matches of the season. Complete the calculations to find out which match had the most supporters altogether.

Match	Team A	Team B
1	3264	2337
2	2189	1834
3	1976	2735
4	2823	1977
5	2028	3269

Match 1
```
  3264
+ 2337
_____
 5591
```

Match 2
```
  2189
+ 1834
_____
```

Match 3
```
  1976
+ 2735
_____
```

Match 4
```
  2823
+ 1977
_____
```

Match 5
```
  2028
+ 3269
_____
```

The match with the most supporters was:

....

For one of the matches, Sam uses rounding to the nearest 100 to estimate that there were 4000 spectators in total. Which of the matches was he estimating and how do you know?

....

At another match, there are 2346 fans for the home team and 1629 fans for the away team. Sam says this is about 3900 people. His dad says it is about 4000. How did they arrive at different estimations?

....

....

....

....

Answers on page 32

These are the supporter numbers for the following three matches.
Complete the calculations then circle the team with the most supporters.

Match	Team A	Team B
6	2187	1793
7	1862	3436
8	3246	2058

Team A
```
  2187
  1862
+ 3246
_____

_____
```

Team B
```
  1793
  3436
+ 2058
_____

_____
```

Sam noticed there is some mud splattered over some of his workings for two of the matches. Can you work out the digits that are covered in mud? Use the correct stickers from your sticker sheet.

```
    2  7  ▓  5
 +  ▓  4  4  ▓
 _____
    4  ▓  1  3
```

```
    3  ▓  1  ▓
 +  2  6  ▓  7
 _____
    ▓  9  0  1
```

For the final match of the season, there are 1845 fans for team A and 1999 fans for team B. Dad says Sam could find the total spectators using a mental method. How could you do it mentally?

Answers on page 32

PARENT TIP: Get your child to throw a dice 8 times to make two 4 digit numbers, then add the two numbers together. Then ask them to try rearranging the digits to make two new 4 digit numbers. Can they make a bigger total than before?

Subtracting 4-digit numbers

The Bailey family are looking at holidays online. Below are the prices for a family of four to different locations:

Italy £1859

Egypt £1679

Jamaica £3058

Florida £3725

They compare the prices using subtraction to find the difference. Can you help them? How much more expensive is:

a Florida than Jamaica?

```
  3725
- 3058
------
  6733
```

b Jamaica than Italy?

```
  3058
- 1859
------
  2801
```

c Italy than Egypt?

```
  1859
- 1679
------
   220
```

d Mr Bailey has £1549 saved. How much more would he need to save to book a holiday to Jamaica? Fill in the boxes to complete the calculation.

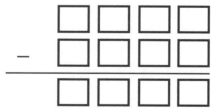

e The family have set a budget of £4500. How much would they have left to spend away if they went to Italy?

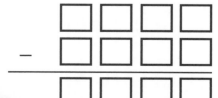

Answers on page 32

The family have decided to go to Florida and have a budget of £2450 for excursions.

f) If they go to the theme park, how much will be left for other excursions?

$$
\begin{array}{r}
2450 \\
- 1265 \\
\hline
 \\
\end{array}
$$

Family ticket prices	
Theme park pass	£1265
Sealife attraction	£189
Wildlife park	£248
Water park	£162
Film studios	£298
Space centre	£164
Dolphin encounter	£329

They pay for the theme park, then choose the other days out. How much will they have left after each trip? Use the remaining money each time.

g) **Wildlife park**

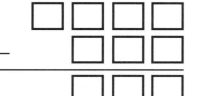

h) **Space centre**

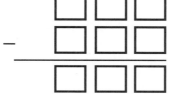

i) **Film studios**

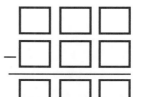

j) **Dolphin encounter**

k) Do they have enough money left to visit the water park? Circle your answer.

yes / no

Mr Bailey compares the visitors to the Water park and the Wildlife park in January and July by finding the difference. He thinks he's made some mistakes so he uses addition to check. Complete his addition checks for him, then explain what he did wrong.

Wildlife park

January: 6325   July: 9164

Mr Bailey's working	Addition check
9164	6325
− 6325	+ 3241
3241	

Water park

January: 5126   July: 7823

Mr Bailey's working	Addition check
7823	5126
− 5126	+ 2703
2703	

Answers on page 32

Using times tables facts

Luke collects stickers and likes to arrange them by theme in his sticker album in arrays. He has 3 rows of 6 animal-themed stickers which he writes as 3 x 6.

3 x 6

He could have arranged his 18 stickers in different arrays. Use the stickers to complete two more arrays in this box, then label them with their multiplication facts.

10

Answers on page 32

Luke uses Factor Rainbows to help him find all the ways he could arrange the 60 stickers in his sticker album.

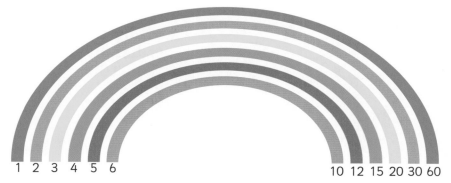

1 2 3 4 5 6   10 12 15 20 30 60

Luke gets 12 more stickers, making 72 stickers in total. Complete the factor rainbow to see how he could arrange them in his sticker album.

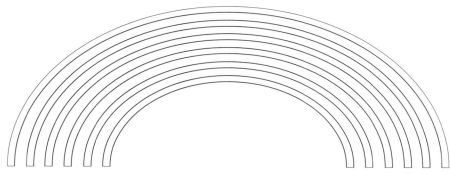

Luke and his friend Ella are comparing how many stickers they have. Write the correct symbol (>, < or =) to show who has more stickers in each theme.

(a) Football stickers

4 x 7 ☐ 8 x 3

(b) Dinosaur stickers

5 x 9 ☐ 9 x 7

(c) Space stickers

12 x 4 ☐ 8 x 6

Luke says that if 4 rows of 3 stickers is 12, then he can work out that 40 rows of 3 stickers is 120. Can you use your multiplication facts to help Luke work out how many stickers he would have on these pages?

6 0   x   7 = ...

5   x   3 0 0 = ...

2 0   x   8 0 = ...

Answers on page 32

Multiplying and dividing mentally

Captain Multivide has magical powers. Jack is putting them to the test!

I can multiply and divide any number by 10 or 100!

Complete the table for each number Jack gives Captain Multivide with what you think his answer will be.

Jack's number	Captain Multivide's power	New number
23	× 10	
17	÷ 100	
30	÷ 10	
16	× 100	
12	÷ 10	

Jack whispers his number to Captain Multivide and the Captain secretly carries out his power. Can you read Captain Multivide's mind and say what power he's using to change the number each time?

a) 3.7   37

b) 0.59   59

c) 190   19

Answers on page 32

Something's gone wrong with Captain Multivide's power and all the answers are coming out wrong. Help him get his power back by telling him what he's done wrong.

Jack's number	Captain Multivide's power	New number	What was his mistake?
34	× 100	340	He multiplied by 10 instead of 100.
23	÷ 10	230	
72	× 10	7200	
20	÷ 100	2	
9	÷ 10	0.09	

Captain Multivide's super team mate, Captain Zerone, has powers of his own using 0 and 1. Can you predict his answers?

(d) 2 3 1 × 1 = 231

(e) 3 5 × 0 = 0

(f) 6 2 ÷ 1 = 62

(g) 5 6 0 × 1 = 560

(h) 9 9 ÷ 1 = 99

(i) 3 0 0 0 × 0 = ⋯⋯⋯⋯⋯⋯⋯⋯⋯

I think that when you multiply a number, it always gets bigger.

What would Captain Zerone say about Captain Multivide's theory? Write in his response.

Answers on page 32

13

Multiplying 3-digit numbers

Jackie is a long-distance lorry driver. She has 5 destinations she regularly travels to. She is wondering which destination has contributed the most miles to her milometer. Can you help her work it out?

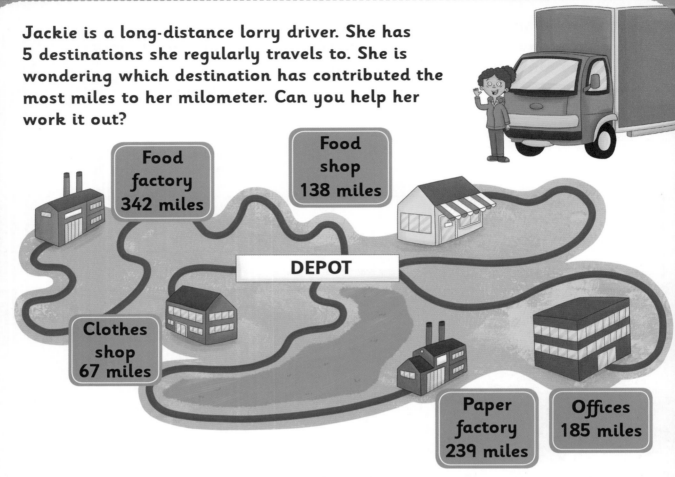

This month, Jackie has driven to the food factory 5 times, the clothes shop 6 times, the paper factory 4 times, the food shop 9 times and the offices 7 times. Can you help her work out how many miles each destination has contributed to her total distance travelled?

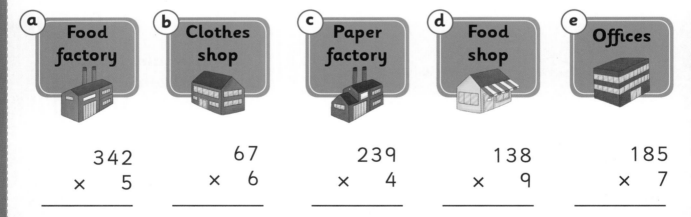

a Food factory
342
× 5
─────

b Clothes shop
67
× 6
─────

c Paper factory
239
× 4
─────

d Food shop
138
× 9
─────

e Offices
185
× 7
─────

Jackie has driven the most miles in total to ....

Answers on page 32

f Every time Jackie fills up with fuel, it costs £248 in petrol. Over a week, she fills up 6 times. How much does she spend on fuel? Use the box for your workings.

g Sometimes Jackie stays overnight in a hotel. The hotel costs £136 per night. This month, she stayed there 7 times. How much money did she spend on the hotel? Use the box for your workings.

Jackie gets paid different rates for different days. She works out her month's pay by multiplying the different day rates by the number of days she's worked at each rate, but she gets oily fingerprints over her workings. Use stickers to fill in the missing digits.

£235 per day for 8 days	£178 per day for 6 days	£186 per day for 5 days

$$2\ 3\ \bullet$$
$$\times \qquad 8$$
$$\overline{1\ \bullet\ 8\ 0}$$

$$\bullet\ 7\ 8$$
$$\times \qquad \bullet$$
$$\overline{1\ 0\ 6\ 8}$$

$$1\ \bullet\ 6$$
$$\times \qquad 5$$
$$\overline{9\ 3\ \bullet}$$

Answers on page 32

PARENT TIP: Take turns with your child to write out a multiplication calculation with a deliberate mistake. Can you and your child spot and explain the mistake you have made?

15

Equivalent fractions

Jeff and Alan are neighbours and have identical rectangular spaces in their gardens to plant vegetables.

Jeff   Alan

The two gardeners split up their vegetable patches into fractions. Write how much of their patch is taken up by each type of vegetable, giving the answer as a fraction in its simplest form.

a Jeff's carrots: ....

b Alan's potatoes: ....

c Jeff's tomatoes: ....

d Alan's tomatoes: ....

e Jeff says that he and Alan have the same fraction of tomatoes. Do you agree? Prove it.

....

....

f Alan says that cabbages take up $\frac{3}{12}$ of his patch. His partner says it is $\frac{1}{4}$. Who is right?

....

g Jeff says that they both have the same fraction of carrots because they both have 2 parts. Show that he is wrong using equivalent fractions.

....

....

Answers on page 32

Alan and Jeff's neighbour across the road, Sally, is planning her own vegetable patch.

Add the missing digits to show what fraction each type of vegetable takes up.

h Potatoes: $\dfrac{3}{}$ **i** Carrots: $\dfrac{}{4}$ **j** Tomatoes: $\dfrac{1}{}$

k Plan your own vegetable patch for this garden. Use stickers to fill the spaces matching the fractions below.

Potatoes: $\dfrac{2}{5}$ Carrots: $\dfrac{1}{4}$ Tomatoes: $\dfrac{1}{5}$

Cabbages: $\dfrac{1}{10}$ Radishes: $\dfrac{1}{20}$

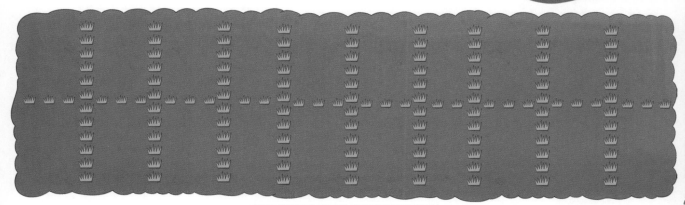

Answers on page 32

PARENT TIP: When cooking, encourage your children to cut up ingredients in different fractional parts. Ask them to describe how they have cut the food up and how many parts have been taken. E.g. "I have cut the cake into eighths. I'm having two pieces so that's a $\dfrac{1}{4}$."

Decimal numbers

Mrs Hanlon is making costumes for the school play. She has lots of fabric and ribbons to cut up. This is how much fabric she needs for each costume:

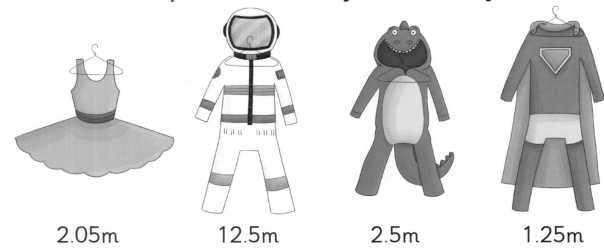

| 2.05m | 12.5m | 2.5m | 1.25m |

Put the costumes from the sticker sheet in order of the length of fabric needed, from least to most.

Her ribbons come in 1m lengths but her pattern gives her the fractions of 1m that she needs. Write the lengths she needs to cut as a decimal number.

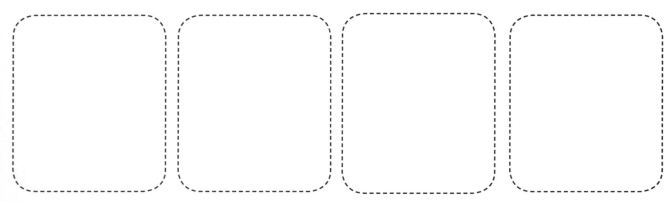

a $\frac{3}{10}$ of red ribbon = ... metres

b $\frac{25}{100}$ of blue ribbon = ... metres

c $\frac{7}{1000}$ of black ribbon = ... metres

Answers on page 32

d) Some children are helping Mrs Hanlon to cut the ribbons. Rebecca reads the instructions, "Cut $\frac{3}{10}$ of a 1m ribbon." She measures 0.03m and is surprised at how short the piece of ribbon is. What did she do wrong?

....

....

Match the decimal that Rebecca should measure to each of these fractions. You can find the decimal stickers on the sticker sheet.

$\frac{2}{100}$ [ ] $\frac{5}{10}$ [ ]

$\frac{5}{100}$ [ ] $\frac{25}{100}$ [ ]

$\frac{20}{100}$ [ ] $\frac{7}{100}$ [ ]

Mrs Hanlon gives Rebecca some numbers to practise ordering. Can you help her choose the correct sign? Use the stickers on your sticker sheet.

$\frac{4}{10}$ [ ] 0.5 $\frac{8}{100}$ [ ] 0.08

0.53 [ ] 0.35   0.17 [ ] $\frac{2}{10}$

0.06 [ ] $\frac{6}{10}$ 0.5 [ ] $\frac{35}{100}$

Answers on page 32

PARENT TIP: Write some decimal numbers with one or two decimal places on sticky notes. Take turns to turn one over at a time. Whoever has the biggest number can keep it. Whoever collects the most numbers wins.

19

Fraction problems

To help pass the time while swimming, Sophie keeps track of the lengths she has swum as fractions.

On Monday, she plans to swim 40 lengths. How many lengths will she have swum after she has done:

a $\frac{1}{10}$ of her lengths? ....

b $\frac{5}{8}$ of her lengths? ....

c $\frac{3}{5}$ of her lengths? ....

d $\frac{3}{4}$ of her lengths? ....

e On Tuesday, she plans to swim 60 lengths. After 22 lengths, she says she has swum more than $\frac{1}{4}$ but less than $\frac{1}{2}$. Do you agree? Why?

....

....

f On Wednesday, she only has time to swim 30 lengths. After swimming for 15 minutes, she has swum $\frac{2}{5}$ of her total lengths. How many lengths has she swum?

....

....

g On Thursday, after swimming 18 lengths, she has swum $\frac{2}{5}$ of her total. How many lengths is she planning to swim?

....

....

Answers on page 32

(h) The following week, Sophie isn't feeling very well and stops swimming before completing her targeted lengths. How many lengths did she swim each day? On which day did she swim the most lengths?

Monday: $\frac{3}{4}$ of 48 lengths   ....

Tuesday: $\frac{2}{3}$ of 60 lengths   ....

Wednesday: $\frac{3}{8}$ of 80 lengths   ....

Sophie swam the most lengths on: ....

(i) The next week, Sophie sets herself a goal of 100 lengths over the whole week. Work out what fraction of these she swam each day.

Monday: 25 lengths   ....

Tuesday: 20 lengths   ....

Wednesday: 10 lengths   ....

Thursday: 30 lengths   ....

Friday: 15 lengths   ....

(j) Sophie swims 40 lengths on Saturday. She says that when she has swum $\frac{1}{3}$ of her total lengths, she will be part way through a lap. Do you agree? Why?

....

(k) Circle the fractions below that will be a complete number of lengths.

$\frac{1}{8}$ $\frac{2}{5}$ $\frac{1}{6}$ $\frac{3}{10}$ $\frac{4}{9}$

Answers on page 32

PARENT TIP: Ask your children, "Would you rather..." and give them two options to choose. For example, $\frac{2}{3}$ of this pile of 12 sweets or $\frac{1}{2}$ of this pile of 20 sweets? Would you rather have $\frac{3}{4}$ of 20 minutes on your tablet or $\frac{5}{6}$ of an hour?

Shape properties

Jake has been researching quadrilaterals on the internet. Can you match his search results to the correct shape? Write the correct letter next to the shapes below.

a
4 equal sides
2 pairs of equal angles
2 pairs of parallel sides
2 lines of symmetry

b
2 pairs of equal sides
4 right angles
2 lines of symmetry

c
2 pairs of equal sides
2 pairs of equal angles
2 pairs of parallel sides
0 lines of symmetry

d
4 equal sides
4 right angles
4 lines of symmetry

 rhombus ○

 equilateral ○

 rectangle ○

 square ○

Jake has written out some properties of triangles, but he's missing some words. Can you fill them in? Use the images to help you.

e .... triangles have two equal sides and two equal angles.

f .... triangles have one right angle and two acute angles.

g .... triangles have all equal angles and all equal sides.

h .... triangles have no equal sides.

isosceles
triangle

right-angled
triangle

equilateral
triangle

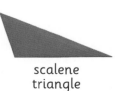
scalene
triangle

Answers on page 32

Jake plays a game with his friend, Billy. He thinks of a shape and describes it to Billy. Billy guesses the shape, but there are two that he's stuck on. Can you help him? Fill in the empty speech bubbles.

(i) It has 4 sides and one line of symmetry. None of the sides are parallel.

....

(j) It has 4 sides and one pair of parallel sides.

....

Jake is wondering if it is always true, sometimes true or never true that...

k. ... quadrilaterals have 4 sides?

l. ... triangles have 2 obtuse angles?

m. ... quadrilaterals have right angles?

Write the answers below and explain why for each one.

k. ....

l. ....

m. ....

Answers on page 32

PARENT TIP: Play Jake's game with your children. Take turns to think of a shape and give clues about it. For example, "My shape has two equal sides and two equal angles." (This would be an isosceles triangle.) Look for shapes in real life and challenge children to name them.

Angles

Alice has been learning about angles at school. She has been asked to find different angles around her home. She notices there are lots of angles on her bike. Can you help her identify which of these angles are obtuse and which are acute? Sort the angles into the table for her.

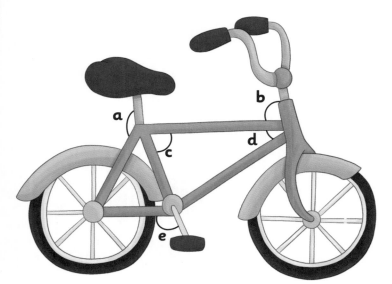

Acute	Obtuse

Alice has drawn a picture of her house and notices more angles. Can you identify them and sort them into the table?

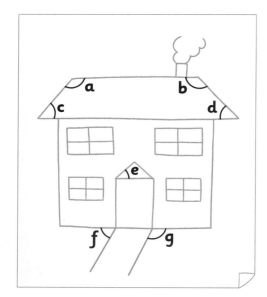

Acute	Obtuse

Answers on page 32

Alice notices that the hands of the clock form angles, too. Can you find the angle in degrees marked between the hands of each clock face?

....

Now use the clock stickers on the sticker sheet to place the angles in order of size from smallest to biggest.

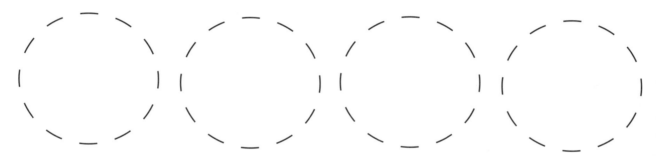

Alice plays a game with her brother. She tells him three facts about the angles inside different shapes and asks him which one is a fib. Can you spot the fib? Put a circle around it then explain why.

(a) A rectangle can never have an acute angle.

(b) A regular hexagon has only obtuse angles.

(c) All the angles of a rhombus are acute.

Answers on page 32

PARENT TIP: Pick up a pile of straws or kebab sticks and drop them on the table. Challenge your child to find as many different acute and obtuse angles between the sticks that cross over as they can. What are there more of, acute or obtuse?

Units of measure

Alex the astronaut is preparing for her journey into space. She needs to get all the supplies ready for the mission.

The table below shows the quantities of different freeze-dried foods Alex and her crew will need each day. Their mission will last **100 days**. How many kilograms of each food should they take? Complete the table.

Food type	Daily quantity	Total in kg
Freeze-dried coffee	35g	
Powdered milk	120g	
Dehydrated vegetables	550g	
Dried biscuits	375g	
Heat-treated tortillas	200g	

(a) Alex estimates that they will need 250ml of lubricant every day to keep the space station's mechanisms working smoothly. How many litres will they need over the 100 day mission?

....

....

(b) The astronauts move around the space station a lot without gravity holding them down. Alex thinks she travels 350m every day. How far does she move each day in kilometres?

....

(c) The astronauts strap themselves down to sleep on their beds. Joe measures the width of his bed and says it is only 0.85m. How wide is this in cm?

....

Answers on page 32

Alex prefers decimal numbers and measures everything in larger units. Joe prefers whole numbers so he uses smaller units of measure. Can you match the equivalent measurements they have each made? The first one has been done for you.

0.06m   600g

0.6m   6cm

6.6m   6600g

0.6kg   660g

0.66kg   660cm

6.6kg   60cm

Alex is trying to teach Joe how different measures relate to each other. Can you help her by finishing her sentences?

(d) There are .... m in 1km so there are .... m in 3km.

(e) There are .... mm in 1cm so there are .... mm in 3cm.

(f) There are .... ml in 1l so there are .... ml in 3l.

(g) There are .... cm in 1m so there are .... cm in 3m.

(h) There are .... g in 1kg so there are .... g in 3kg.

Answers on page 32

Perimeter and area

Kirsty's family are redecorating their house. They need to measure each room for new skirting boards before the new carpets can go in. Can you help Kirsty and her family work out the perimeter and area for each room? Complete the table below.

	Length of room	Width of room	Skirting board perimeter	Carpet area
Dining room	6m	4m		
Kitchen	5m	3m		
Play room	3m	3m		
Bedroom 1	4m	4m		
Bedroom 2	4m	3m		

Kirsty and her family have forgotten to include the spare bedroom! They need 14m of skirting boards and 12m² for the carpet. What could the length and width of the room be?

....

....

Once the garage conversion is finished, they measure the perimeter for the skirting boards. Each wall is a whole number of metres. The total distance they measure is 18m. What could the walls measure?
Can you find three different possible measurements? Write them below.

Answers on page 32

The utility room is a square shape with its area the same as its perimeter. What could the lengths of the walls be? Show your workings out.

....

....

The living room is a rectilinear shape.
What is the total length of skirting board and total area of carpet needed for the living room? Show your workings out.

....

....

....

3m

4m

7m

6m

3m

9m

Answers on page 32

PARENT TIP: Help your children to measure the length and width of the rooms in your house. Which room has the biggest floor area? Which room has the longest perimeter?

29

Telling the time

Dave works at the funfair. He does different jobs all through the day. Write the digital time he does each job in both 12 hour and 24 hour clock times.

 **a** Running the rollercoaster

 **b** Fixing the dodgems

 **c** Selling candyfloss

 d Making balloon animals

am

....

....

am

....

....

pm

....

....

pm

....

....

Dave is running late today and takes his break half an hour after he is supposed to. Show the time on each analogue clock half an hour after he was supposed to take his break.

Morning break

10:25am

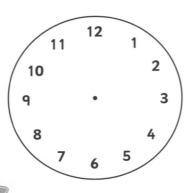

Lunch break

12:45am

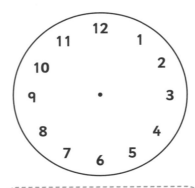

Afternoon break

2:20pm

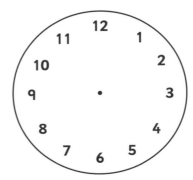

Answers on page 32

The clock in the staff room has lost its minute hand, but Dave says he can still use it to tell the time. Draw lines to match each clock face to the time it shows.

3:30pm

6:15pm

8:30am

2:45pm

Dave has to keep a log of when he closes the rides for cleaning. He writes the times down, but forgets to put them in the right order. Can you help him organise his log? Use the stickers to put the rides in the correct order from earliest to latest.

4:35 pm	Dodgems
11:42 am	Tea cups
3:12 pm	Carousel

09:30	Ferris wheel
15:47	Helter skelter
14:08	Pirate ship

1 ....

2 ....

3 ....

4 ....

5 ....

6 ....

Answers on page 32

Answers

Pages 2–3: Reading and comparing

Jenny: Three thousand and fifty; Mike: Two thousand, two hundred and forty-six; Alice: One thousand, three hundred and fifty-five.

Round 2 scores: Alice: £3355; Jenny: £2550; Mike: £2156, Steve: £2607. Round 3 scores: a. Alice must win £500. b. Jenny needs £600 to catch up with Steve. c. Mike needs to win £700 to pass his target. Alice: the computer added £500 to the total instead of subtracting £500. Jenny: the computer added £3000 instead of £300. Mike: The computer added £40 instead of £50. Steve: the computer subtracted £200 instead of adding £800.

Pages 4–5: Rounding

	Visitor numbers	Rounded to the nearest 10	Rounded to the nearest 100	Rounded to the nearest 1000
January	2345	2350	2300	2000
February	2767	2770	2800	3000
March	3698	3700	3700	4000
April	3064	3060	3100	3000
May	4002	4000	4000	4000
June	2986	2990	3000	3000

	Visitor numbers	Rounded to nearest 10	Rounded to nearest 100	Rounded to nearest 1000
July	2863	2860	2900	3000
August	2638	2640	2600	3000
September	3268	3270	3300	3000

a. the number of visitors could be any numbers between 2250 and 2349 inclusive. b. Highest: 2349, Lowest: 2250. c. Highest: 2449, Lowest: 2350. d. They both round to 4000. e. 3 ones round down to the nearest ten, but the nearest ten happens to be also a multiple of 100. f. 8499.

Pages 6–7: Adding 4-digit numbers

1. 5601, 2. 4023, 3. 4711, 4. 4800, 5. 5297.
Match 1 had the most supporters in total.
Sam was estimating Match 2 by adding 2200 + 1800.
Sam rounded to the nearest 100 while his dad rounded to the nearest 1000.
Team A: 7295. Team B: 7287. Team A had the most supporters.

```
    2 7 6 5          3 2 1 4
  + 1 4 4 8        + 2 6 8 7
  ---------        ---------
    4 2 1 3          5 9 0 1
```

1845 + 2000 − 1 = 384

Pages 8–9: Subtracting 4-digit numbers

a. £667, b. £1199, c. £180.

```
d.   3 0 5 8     e.   4 5 0 0     f.   2 4 5 0
   - 1 5 4 9        - 1 8 5 9        - 1 2 6 5
   ---------        ---------        ---------
     1 5 0 9          2 6 4 1          1 1 8 5

     1 1 8 5          9 3 7            7 7 3          4 7 5
   -   2 4 8        - 1 6 4          - 2 9 8        - 3 2 9
   ---------        -----            -----          -----
       9 3 7          7 7 3            4 7 5          1 4 6
```

No.
Addition checks: Wildlife park: 9566, Water park: 7829. Mr Bailey made the mistake of always subtracting the smaller digit in each column from the larger digit.

Pages 10–11: Using times tables facts

Possible arrays are: 1 row of 18 stickers (1 x 18), 2 rows of 9 stickers (2 x 9), 3 rows of 6 stickers (3 x 6), 6 rows of 3 stickers (6 x 3), 9 rows of 2 stickers (9 x 2). 18 rows of 1 sticker (18 x 1).

a. >, b. <, c. =, d. 420, e. 1500, f. 1600.

Pages 12–13: Multiplying and dividing mentally

Jack's number	Captain Multivide's power	New number
23	× 10	230
17	÷ 100	0.17
30	÷ 10	3
16	× 100	1600
12	÷ 10	1.2

a. × 10, b. × 100, c. ÷ 10

Jack's number	Captain Multivide's power	New number	What was his mistake?
34	× 100	340	He multiplied by 10 instead of 100.
23	÷ 10	230	He multiplied by 10 instead of dividing.
72	× 10	7200	He multiplied by 100 instead of 10.
20	÷ 100	2	He divided by 10 instead of 100.
9	÷ 10	0.09	He divided by 100 instead of 10.

d. 231, e. 0, f. 62, g. 560. h. 99, i. 0
Numbers multiplied by 1 stay the same size and don't get bigger. Numbers multiplied by 0 always become 0.

Pages 14–15: Multiplying 3-digit numbers

a. 1710, b. 402, c. 956, d. 1242, e. 1295. Jackie drove the most miles to the food factory. f. £1488, g. £952.

```
    2 3 5          1 7 8          1 8 6
  ×     8        ×     6        ×     5
  -------        -------        -------
  1 8 8 0        1 0 6 8          9 3 0
```

Pages 16–17: Equivalent fractions

a. $\frac{1}{3}$, b. $\frac{1}{4}$, c. $\frac{1}{6}$, d. $\frac{1}{6}$, e. Jeff has $\frac{1}{6}$ and Alan has $\frac{2}{12}$ which can be simplified to $\frac{1}{6}$. f. Both are right: $\frac{3}{12} = \frac{1}{4}$. g. Jeff has $\frac{2}{6}$ (= $\frac{1}{3}$), but Alan has $\frac{2}{12} = \frac{1}{6}$. h. $\frac{3}{8}$, i. $\frac{1}{4}$, j. $\frac{1}{8}$.

Other arrangements are possible.

Pages 18–19: Decimal numbers

a. 0.3m, b. 0.25m, c. 0.007m, d. $\frac{3}{10}$ = 0.3m, not 0.03m. $\frac{2}{100}$ = 0.02, $\frac{5}{100}$ = 0.05, $\frac{20}{100}$ = 0.2, $\frac{5}{10}$ = 0.5, $\frac{25}{100}$ = 0.25, $\frac{7}{10}$ = 0.07. $\frac{4}{10}$ < 0.5, $\frac{8}{100}$ = 0.08, 0.53 > 0.35, 0.17 < $\frac{2}{10}$, 0.06 < $\frac{6}{10}$, 0.5 > $\frac{35}{100}$.

Pages 20–21: Fraction problems

a. 4, b. 25, c. 24, d. 30. e. Yes. $\frac{1}{4}$ of 60 = 15 and $\frac{1}{2}$ of 60 = 30. 22 is between 15 and 30. f. 12. g. 45. h. Monday: 36, Tuesday: 40, Wednesday: 30 lengths. Sophie swam the most lengths on Tuesday. i. Monday: $\frac{1}{4}$. Tuesday: $\frac{1}{5}$, Wednesday: $\frac{1}{10}$, Thursday: $\frac{3}{10}$, Friday: $\frac{3}{20}$. j. Yes. 3 doesn't divide equally into 40. k. $\frac{1}{8}$, $\frac{2}{5}$, $\frac{3}{10}$ all make a complete number of lengths.

Pages 22–23: Shape properties

a. ◆ b. ▬ c. ▱ d. ▬

e. Isosceles, f. Right-angled, g. Equilateral, h. Scalene. i. Kite j. Trapezium. k. Always true: quad means 4. l. Never true: they can have one obtuse angle. m. Sometimes true: e.g. a square does, a rhombus doesn't.

Pages 24–25: Angles

Bike: Acute: b, c, d. Obtuse: a, e. House: Acute: c, d, e, f. Obtuse: a, b, g. Clocks: half past 3: 75°, 8 o' clock: 120°, 11 o' clock: 30°, half past 7: 45°.

a. True. b. True. c. False: 2 are acute and 2 are obtuse.

Pages 26–27: Units of measure

Freeze dried coffee: 3.5kg, Powdered milk: 12kg, Dehydrated vegetables: 55kg, Dried biscuits: 37.5kg, Heat treated tortillas: 20kg. a. 25 litres, b. 0.35km, c. 85cm.
0.06m – 6cm, 0.6m – 60cm, 6.6m – 660cm, 0.6kg – 600g, 0.66kg – 660g, 6.6kg – 6600g.
d. 1000, 3000, e. 10, 30, f. 1000, 3000, g. 100, 300, h. 1000, 3000.

Pages 28–29: Perimeter and area

Dining room: 20m, 24m², Kitchen: 16m, 15m², Play room: 12m, 9m², Bedroom 1: 16m, 16m², Bedroom 2: 14m, 12m². Spare bedroom: 4m x 3m Possible pairs of measurements include: 5m x 4m, 6m x 3m, 7m x 2m, 8m x 1m. Utility room: 4m. Living room: 32m of skirting board, 39m² of carpet.

Pages 30–31: Telling the Time

a. 8:30am, 08:30, b. 11:15am, 11:15, c. 1:30pm, 13:30, d. 3:40pm, 15:40.

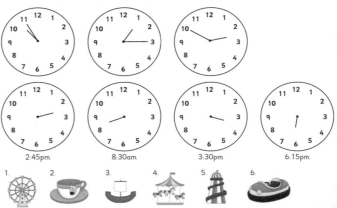

2:45pm   8:30am   3:30pm   6:15pm

1.   2.   3.   4.   5.   6.